Andrew Brodie

Supporting Writing

FOR AGES 12–13

Contents

Introduction

The *Supporting Writing* series is aimed at all those who work with students who have been identified as needing 'additional' or 'different' literacy support. It can be used by anyone working with children who fall into this category, whether you are a teacher, classroom assistant or parent.

Typically, the twelve to thirteen year-old students, for whom the book is intended, will be working at the levels expected of Year 6 or Year 7 pupils or they may simply need extra help in tackling the level of work appropriate for Year 8. Their difficulties may be short-term, and overcome with extra practice and support on a one-to-one or small group basis, or they may be long-term, where such support enables them to make progress but at a level behind their peer group.

The activities in this book provide exactly what these students need – plenty of writing activities linked to their work in other aspects of literacy. All the activities provide excellent opportunities for speaking and listening, and these sometimes include simple drama activities based on role-play. Most pages include reading practice in addition to the main writing task. Each activity page includes brief teachers' notes so that the pages can be picked up and used quickly and effectively.

This book is divided into eight sections:

Section 1 is concerned with writing speech, both in the form of scripts and in correctly punctuated prose. Worksheets 1 to 6 provide many opportunities for role-play as well as for writing speech appropriately. Students are given 'rules' to follow regarding the punctuation of speech. Worksheet 7, the final sheet of the section, requires the students to write a story, or part of a story, that begins with a short burst of speech.

Section 2, on Worksheets 8 to 12, is designed to encourage students to take meaningful notes. Examples of notes and follow-up practice activities are provided. Hopefully students will be able to extend this work by making use of their note-taking skills across other curriculum subjects.

Section 3 looks at the language of advertising, specifically the vocabulary and abbreviations used by estate agents. Worksheets 13 to 16 ask students to write descriptively about a house, in the style of an estate agent.

Section 4, on Worksheets 17 to 20, considers writing for a variety of purposes and audiences. A short story written as a dialogue is examined carefully before students retell the same story in three different ways: as simple prose, as a comic strip and as a newspaper report.

Section 5, Worksheets 21 and 22, helps students to make writing more exciting by careful use of adjectives and by the use of extra text, that can be added to sentences between bracketing commas.

Section 6, addresses the process of planning a story. This section asks students to gather ideas for where a story could take place, when it could take place, who could be involved and what style or genre could be used. On Worksheet 27, the students gather the ideas together then plan the structure of the story before planning further details using Worksheets 28 to 30. Finally, the students should produce a finished story through the full process of planning, drafting, editing, revising, proofreading and 'publishing'.

Section 7, on Worksheets 31 and 32, presents opportunities to write for different purposes. On Worksheet 31 students are encouraged to present balanced arguments in their writing regarding whether thirteen year-olds should be able to choose their own bedtimes. On Worksheet 32 they are presented with a formal letter that demonstrates a writer's attempts to argue persuasively and are then asked to write a similar letter, in a formal or informal style.

Section 8 has:

- three writing templates that are designed to be paper-clipped behind plain sheets of paper to give clear guidelines for writing prose and informal or formal letters
- an Alphabet practice sheet to improve alphabetical order skills
- a Word-finding practice sheet
- Dictionary resource sheets that can be photocopied to create a personal dictionary. Once printed on paper, students should be able to fold it into a booklet and carry it in their blazer pockets or in their bags so that they can make use of it in their other lessons.

The dictionary contains the more challenging of the high and medium frequency words recommended for Key Stages 1 and 2, together with the words recommended for students in the early part of secondary school. We have deliberately included words that are not phonically regular.

Each page of the dictionary has spaces for the students to write their own spellings – this is an excellent way of encouraging the students to use their phonic knowledge to spell new words.

Students generally achieve the greatest success in an atmosphere of support and encouragement. Praise from a caring adult can be the best reward for the students' efforts. The worksheets and activities in this book will provide many opportunities for students to enjoy these successes. The development of a positive attitude and the resulting increase in self-esteem will help them with all of their schoolwork.

Record and Review

Name: ______________________ Date of birth: __________

Teacher: ______________________ Class: __________

Support Assistant: ______________________

Code of Practice stage: ______________________ Date targets set: __________

Target

1 ______________________

2 ______________________

3 ______________________

4 ______________________

Review

Target

1 ______________________

____

______________________ Target achieved? ☐ Date __________

2 ______________________

____

______________________ Target achieved? ☐ Date __________

3 ______________________

____

______________________ Target achieved? ☐ Date __________

4 ______________________

____

______________________ Target achieved? ☐ Date __________

Writing speech

Notes for teachers

This section provides an opportunity to get to know new students while reminding them that speech can be written in the form of a script or as appropriately punctuated prose.

The first two worksheets feature question and answer scripts and students should be shown that speech marks are not necessary for speech written in this way. Encourage the students to act out the interview, developing their confidence in speaking and listening as well as in thinking creatively.

Worksheet 3 introduces the types of words that frequently appear at the start of questions and students are again asked to think creatively by inventing some questions that they could ask a friend. Worksheets 4-6 provide further practice of this. Many students still struggle to remember capital letters and full stops. Looking closely at the punctuation required to show speech provides useful opportunities for revising the use of capital letters, full stops, commas, exclamation marks and question marks. Some students will find it difficult to think of all the questions on Worksheet 5 and you could help them to present the work as a dictation rather than a creative exercise. The text for the dictation is:

> *"Would you like an ice cream?" asked Sam.*
> *"Oh, yes please," said Mum.*
> *"A large one or a small one?"*
> *"Just a small one please," insisted Mum.*
> *"What flavour would you like?"*
> *"Vanilla," replied Mum.*
> *"Would you like a flake with it?" asked Sam.*
> *"No, thank you," answered Mum.*

Encourage them to notice that:
- (i) The words spoken are contained between the speech marks;
- (ii) Every sentence starts with a capital letter;
- (iii) The sentences do not end at the end of the spoken section;
- (iv) The closing speech marks are never alone – they always have a full stop, a comma, an exclamation mark or a question mark before them;
- (v) Different words are used before the speaker's name e.g. *said, asked, replied.*
- (vi) A new line is started where a different person speaks.

Worksheet 7 provides the opportunity to create a longer piece of writing in the form of a short story.

Several additional aspects of literacy will be addressed by working through this section:
- There are valuable opportunities for speaking and listening in the form of simple drama activities that can be used to strengthen students' awareness of written speech.
- Students are encouraged to write creatively, composing their own conversations.
- Students are introduced to a range of appropriate vocabulary to use with speech.

Tell me about you

Worksheet 1

Name ______________________

- Imagine that you are being interviewed on the radio or T.V. The interviewer is asking you the questions shown below. Work with a partner to practise the answers that you would give. The first time you try it you may find that you hesitate and say things like 'er' or 'um'. Keep trying until you feel that you sound confident.

"

Interviewer: Could you start by telling me your name?

Interviewer: When is your birthday and how old are you now?

Interviewer: Which school do you attend and what year are you in?

Interviewer: Are there any lessons that you particularly like?

Interviewer: Are there any lessons that you particularly dislike?

Interviewer: Do you attend any school clubs or activities?

Interviewer: Who are your closest friends?

Interviewer: Where do you live?

Interviewer: How do you travel to school?

Interviewer: What do you like doing outside of school?

Interviewer: Describe your home and family.

Interviewer: What are your hopes for the future?

"

Notes for teachers

This worksheet provides lots of opportunities for getting to know new students. Discuss the instructions thoroughly before helping them to read the interview questions. Encourage the students to work in pairs, taking turns to play the roles of the interviewer and interviewee. Assure them that they will become more confident as they practise. When they are ready they could record their interviews using either audio or video equipment. Explain that the interviewer's questions are shown on this worksheet in the form of a play script and that they can record their written answers on Worksheet 2.

The interview

Worksheet 2

Name ______

Here are some of the questions asked by your interviewer. Write your answers.

"

Interviewer: Could you start by telling me your name?

______

Interviewer: Which school do you attend and what year are you in?

______

Interviewer: Are there any lessons that you particularly like?

______

Interviewer: Are there any lessons that you particularly dislike?

______

Interviewer: Do you attend any school clubs or activities?

______

Interviewer: Where do you live?

______

Interviewer: How do you travel to school?

______

Interviewer: What are your hopes for the future?

______

"

Notes for teachers

This worksheet follows Worksheet 1 and is designed for students to record their written answers to the interviewer's questions. Help them to write on this page in the form of a script, following the pattern set by the interviewer's questions. As the punctuation style of a script is not very demanding you could encourage them to use this opportunity to practise writing neatly in a fast fluent style.

Questions

Worksheet 3

Name ______

- Look again at the questions on Worksheet 1. Although we describe them as 'interview questions', one of them is not actually a question as it is an instruction. Write out this instruction.

- Now look at all the other questions. Each one ends with a question mark. Write down the *start* word of each question.

- Which of these words are used at the beginning of more than one of the questions?

- Notice that several of the *start* words begin with the letter **w**. Write these here:

- Invent questions that you could ask a friend, using each of the **w** words above.

Notes for teachers

This worksheet provides opportunities for reading practice while identifying words that typically appear at the beginning of questions. The final task is to create a set of questions. It would be ideal if the students could put these questions to a friend.

Questions and answers

Worksheet 4

Name ______________________

- Look at this pair of sentences:

  "How are you today?" asked the doctor.

  "Much better," replied the old lady.

Write a suitable reply to each of the following questions. You will need to invent some characters to answer the questions and you will need to be creative in thinking up answers.

"What are you doing on Saturday?" asked Wayne.

____

"Where are you going?" asked the teacher.

____

"When are you going to do your homework?" demanded Mum.

____

"How many people are in your family?" enquired the nurse.

____

- Try writing some sentence pairs of your own.

____

____

____

____

____

____

____

____

Notes for teachers

The interview shown on Worksheets 1 and 2 was written in the form of a script. On this sheet the introductory pair of sentences is written as punctuated speech. The students may need to be reminded of the 'rules' for written speech before attempting to create their own answers to the questions.

Answers

Worksheet 5

Name ________________

Read these sentences. They are all answers to questions that were asked during a conversation.

"Oh, yes please," said Mum.

"Just a small one please," insisted Mum.

"Vanilla," replied Mum.

"No, thank you," answered Mum.

Can you work out what the questions were? They are all part of the same conversation. Try to write out the whole conversation, showing the questions and the answers.

Notes for teachers

Unlike Worksheet 4, the short conversation on this page is a complete conversation rather than separate isolated pairs of sentences. Again, the students may need to be reminded of the 'rules' for written speech.

Conversation

Worksheet 6

Name ____________________

Remember the rules for punctuating written speech:

1. The words spoken are contained between speech marks.
2. Every sentence starts with a capital letter.
3. The sentences do not end at the end of the spoken section.
4. The closing speech marks are never alone – they always have a comma, an exclamation mark, a full stop or a question mark before them.
5. Different words are used before the speaker's name – for example, 'said', 'asked', 'replied'.
6. A new line is started when a different person speaks.

Try to imagine a conversation that could take place between a parent and a teenager. Perhaps the teenager wants to stay up late or go out with a friend. When you are ready, write out this conversation.

Notes for teachers

Read through the 'rules' with the students then ask them to imagine the conversation. They could work in pairs, with one playing the role of the adult and the other playing the teenager, to enable them to role play the conversation first. Observe how they complete the written task, reminding them of the rules as they work.

Story starters

Worksheet 7

Name ____________________

"Leave me alone!" shouted Tom.

- The line above is the start of a story – your task is to write more of the story.
  a) You need to decide to whom Tom is speaking: it could be his mum, a bully, his brother or sister, etc.
  b) You need to decide why he is shouting and why he wants to be left alone.
  c) You may need to consider where he is and when the story is taking place.
  d) You may decide to include more speech or to continue the story without any further speech.
- When your story is ready show a friend or, if you are feeling brave, see if you can read it out to the group!

Notes for teachers

Read through the instructions with the students, discussing the decisions that need to be made.

Writing notes

Notes for teachers

This section is designed to help students to take meaningful notes that they can refer to later. This is a skill that many students find very difficult.

Worksheets 8 and 9 feature some information supplied by a teacher regarding the *Black Death* and the corresponding notes written by pupils. The students' task is to match the notes to the information and, in doing so, to identify effective and ineffective notes based on the information provided.

Worksheet 10 is designed to encourage students to think of many commonly used ways to abbreviate words and phrases to speed up note taking. This work can also serve as a starting point to compile a class bank of abbreviations. This could include texting short-form signs and symbols.

Worksheet 11 has some sample notes for students to discuss. It is important that they recognise the significance of being able to interpret what is in each note, that they realise that note **e** is written too fully, hence, would take too much time and that note **c** may not have enough in it to make sense. (Note **c** was meant to reflect that all dogs, including our domestic pets, have descended from the wolf – but would the student who wrote it remember this fact when the notes were actually used?).

Worksheet 12 provides some clear tips on how to take notes, together with a short but challenging passage on which students can make notes.

After completing the work on these pages it is important to provide students with frequent opportunities in class to write notes.

Written notes 1

Worksheet 8

Name ______________________

Year 8 were having a history lesson, learning about some of the events that occurred in Medieval England. The teacher was telling them about the 'Black Death'.

The teacher asked the students to write notes on what she was saying so that they could later use the information to write an essay for their homework.

Below are some of the notes. Cut out the notes and match them to the sentences on Worksheet 9.

Parents left sick chn.

B.D. came from China.

London = crowded st, sewage, filth – disease spread fast.

Began Eng autumn 1348

Boats – blk rats – fleas

Plague affected all

1.5 mill pple died in eng 1348–1350 (3yrs)

V. old, V young and poor died first.

Ppl died within week.

$\frac{1}{3}$ – $\frac{1}{2}$ of popn died.

Notes for teachers

Help the students to read the notes and to attempt to interpret them. Discuss what the abbreviations could mean and whether they are effective as abbreviations. When you feel that the students are ready, ask them to cut out the notes on this sheet and the sentences on Worksheet 9 and match them up.

Written notes 2

Worksheet 9

Name ______________________

The sentences below show what the teacher told Year 8 about the *Black Death*. Cut out the sentences and match them to the notes on Worksheet 8.

The 'Black Death' arrived in England in the autumn of 1348.

The disease had begun in central China and spread across Asia and into southern Europe before arriving in England.

This Plague came from fleas that had lived on black rats that came here on merchant ships.

Plague victims usually died within a week of showing symptoms of the illness.

This meant that between a third and a half of the population had been killed by the illness.

In London the crowded filthy conditions, which included sewage running along the streets, helped the disease to spread very rapidly.

The first people to be affected by the Black Death were the very young, the very old and the poor as they were weaker.

Soon all sections of society, including the rich, were dying.

Sick children were often abandoned by their parents, as parents knew they could do nothing to save their children and they might become infected themselves if they stayed with them.

During the three years of the plague (1348 to 1350) one and a half million people were infected and consequently died.

Notes for teachers

Help the students to read the sentences ensuring that they understand what each one means. When you feel that they are ready, ask the students to cut out the sentences and to match them to the notes from Worksheet 8. Once they have done so, collect in the notes and ask the students to attempt their own notes for the sentences – who can write the shortest notes that still make sense and still contain the relevant information?

Abbreviations

Worksheet 10

Name ____________________

In the first box are some words, phrases and titles. In the second box are abbreviations or other shortened versions that you might use if you were making notes. Write them in their correct pairs – the first one has been done for you. You will need to continue on the back of this sheet or in an exercise book.

two and for example October Royal Air Force Road doctor Saint
as well as (plus) kilograms Bed and Breakfast before triangle
Royal Society for the Prevention of Cruelty to Animals possibly
equals (is the same as) Thursday World War happy/pleased
rhinoceros ninety-nine February television

Thur + Rd. TV Feb △ poss St. b4 ☺ & rhino
R.A.F R.S.P.C.A. kg. 99 WW Oct. Dr. 2 B & B = e.g.

R.S.P.C.A.	Royal Society for the Prevention of Cruelty to Animals.

Discuss other abbreviations that you know. You could make a class 'bank' of abbreviations that can be used to help with writing notes.

Notes for teachers

Help the students to read through the words, phrases and titles before asking them to match them to the abbreviations.

Worksheet 11

Reading notes

Name ______________________

A class watched an information film about caring for dogs. They were asked to take notes to use the following week in school. Below are some notes that were written by some of the students. Read the notes and decide which you think were good and why. Discuss your ideas with a partner and be ready to share them with the rest of the group.

a) Dgs eat meat.

b) It is important to brush a dog carefully each day to ensure a shiny healthy coat.

c) All d's from wolves.

d) Brush every day = good coat.

e) Dogs for difrent things – racing, garding, herding,

f) RSPCA rescue – treat – rehome.

g) D's like 2 b walked, brushed, stroked, fed, etc evry day.

One of the above is a full sentence and is not in note form at all – for this reason it is not a very good 'note'. Notes should be brief and should contain the important pieces of information so that they can be changed to full sentences when needed. Choose four of the notes above and change them to full sentences.

____

____

____

____

____

____

____

____

Notes for teachers

It is important that the students realise that notes should be short but meaningful so that they make sense when re-read. Ensure that they have correctly identified note **b** as the sentence that has not been shortened effectively. Discuss the words that have been abbreviated in such a way that they are no longer spelt correctly and help them to find the correct spellings.

Writing notes

Worksheet 12

Name ______________________

- When you are writing notes there are several things to remember that will make the note taking easier and will make your notes more useful when you use them later.

1. Don't write any words that are not needed.
2. Use shortened forms of words or abbreviations when possible. (You could always use texting short-form if you like.)
3. Arrange your notes clearly so that they are easy to read later.
4. Don't worry too much about spellings or super neatness – just make sure you can understand what you meant to say. (You can always use a dictionary later!)
5. The subject of your work can, after being written once, just be initials e.g. if you are taking notes on *electricity* you might decide to just use a capital **E** to represent the word *electricity* in your notes.
6. Remember: the most important thing about taking notes is that you should be able to read them easily later.

- Read the passage below then make notes on it. Try to write as little as possible but make sure that you keep the main facts.

We generally think of electricity as the flow of power. However, we must not forget static electricity where a charge builds up and can create some interesting effects. For example rubbing a balloon on your clothes can cause it to build up an electrical charge so that you can attach the balloon to a wall.
We can create a flow of electricity by converting other sources of energy such as water, wind, oil, coal and nuclear power. These sources are called primary sources of energy, whilst the electricity gained from converting these is a secondary source of energy.

____

____

____

____

Notes for teachers

Read through the note-taking guidance with the students before presenting them with the short passage about electricity. Help them to read the passage, ensuring that they understand the vocabulary.

Writing for advertising purposes

Notes for teachers

This section is designed to help students consider the effect of the language they use on their writing. It is tackled in a light-hearted yet thought-provoking way, through the world of advertising. The first section deals with the type of language estate agents use in their need to present a positive image of the properties they are selling.

The work in this section is greatly enhanced by showing students house sale adverts in the local newspaper. In addition to this, you could provide students with house details from a local estate agent so they can study the design and layout. The section also lends itself to some cross-curricular work. When students are asked to create a set of property details for their own home you could ask them to research the age of the house, some of the architectural details and the correct measurements of rooms. (In some circumstances it may be more appropriate to ask students to create details of a house that is not their own.)

Worksheet 13 draws students' attention to the fact that there are many phrases used to describe aspects of a house that are literally true, but do not mean exactly what one might expect e.g. 'cosy' may be a positive way of saying that a room is small. They are encouraged to notice that a particular style of writing will be used for a particular purpose – in this case the style is that of an estate agent whose aim is to sell or let a home.

Worksheet 14 contains four pictures of the same house. Pupils are asked to discuss the pictures in preparation for Worksheets 15 and 16, which feature activities on writing advertisements and estate agent style details about the house.

An extension to this section would be to look at adverts for confectionery and how the language dwells on taste and imagery but ignores the lack of nutritional value. Another way of continuing the work on the language and, where appropriate, abbreviations of adverts would be to look at job vacancy adverts or those for second-hand cars. Students can thoroughly enjoy using the language of one type of advert to sell something else e.g. using 'confectionery language' to sell cars!

Moving house

Worksheet 13

Name ______________________

When people are looking for a new house they will usually go to an estate agent who is handling the sale or letting of a variety of properties. The estate agent advertises each house in such a way that people are interested in seeing, and possibly buying or renting it. To do this, the agent always includes the best features of the house in the advert, and may not mention aspects of the house that could put off potential customers.

Adverts must always be truthful, but careful use of language can make a house sound better than it really is.

Below are examples of some words and phrases that are often used in house descriptions and what each of them might actually mean. Try to match each description to its possible meaning. The first one has been done for you.

Advertising description	Possible meaning
unique	clean, tidy and recently decorated inside
magnificent	old
period property	by a noisy main road
character accommodation	unusual layout inside
cosy	very unusual (this is not always a good thing)
easy access to town	small
well presented	large and expensive

Write a short description of an imaginary house using some of the language from the left-hand column above. You will need to write in complete sentences.

Now write a short description of the same house using some of the language from the right-hand column above. Again, make sure that you write in complete sentences.

Notes for teachers

This page provides an excellent opportunity for reading practice and vocabulary development, as well as for revision of punctuation. Help the students to read the instructions and the information in the table, and then to write creative descriptions.

House for sale 1

Worksheet 14

Name ______________________

- On this page there are four photos of a house and garden, in East Anglia. The house has three bedrooms and is semi-detached. Next to each photo is some information about the house.
- Look at the photos and discuss them with a partner or the group. Discuss what things you are not told about the house, whether you would or would not like to live in this house, and why.

Front view of house

Rear view of house from back garden

View of back garden

View through kitchen (measuring approximately 2.2m x 3.2m) into entrance hall

Notes for teachers

Encourage the students to discuss the house photos before they attempt the written activity on Worksheet 15. You may like to prompt the students, particularly when identifying the facts that are 'not known' about the house: its location, whether it has a garage, whether it has good views, whether it is in a town, city, village, whether it is on a busy thoroughfare or in a quiet cul-de-sac, etc.

Abbreviations and house descriptions

Worksheet 15

Name ____________________

When house adverts are placed in the newspaper, abbreviations are often used to enable as many details as possible to be included.

Choose the correct word or words to write by each of the abbreviations below.

garage lounge conservatory entrance hall
bathroom utility room garden shower detached
central heating location bungalow cloakroom room

Bthrm. ____________________ Bung. ____________________
C\htg. ____________________ Clk. ____________________
Consv. ____________________ Det. ____________________
Ent. Hall ____________________ Gge. ____________________
Gdn. ____________________ Lnge. ____________________
Loc. ____________________ Rm. ____________________
Shwr. ____________________ Utl Rm. ____________________

Now look again at the photos on Worksheet 14. Cut out one of the photos then write a very short advert that could appear in a newspaper as if the house was for sale or to let. You may need to use some of the abbreviations so that your advert fits in the space provided.

Stick the photograph here

____
____
____
____

Notes for teachers

Help the students read and follow the instructions. Encourage them to realise that the advert will not contain full sentences so the information must be abbreviated.

House for sale 2

Worksheet 16

Name ______________________

Stick in the other photos from Worksheet 14 and write full details of each feature of the house, as if you are the estate agent wanting to sell it. Think carefully about the layout of your work and which details are the most important to include.

Stick the photograph here

____
____
____
____
____
____

____
____
____
____
____
____

Stick the photograph here

Stick the photograph here

____
____
____
____
____
____

Notes for teachers

If possible show the students some real estate agents' details for a house, then encourage them to write similar details about three features of the house shown in the photographs. As an extension activity the students could write the full details for a house that they know well, presented in the style of an estate agent.

SECTION 4

Writing for different purposes

Notes for teachers

This section looks at writing for a variety of purposes and audiences. The work provides an introduction to writing dialogue, writing a narrative for younger readers, writing a comic strip and composing a newspaper article. Each part of this section has potential for being extended and developed with a group of students.

Worksheet 17 features a dialogue between two friends. This dialogue forms the basis for the work on the following pages. It can also be used for follow-up work on writing dialogue.

Worksheet 18 asks students to retell the story that is portrayed in the dialogue. They are told to write for an audience of nine year olds to encourage clear basic descriptive writing and to allow for the addition of meaningful illustrations. It is important to make sure students understand that this task does not need dialogue. They should also know that they can add detail to make the writing as interesting as possible.

Worksheet 19 asks students to change the dialogue into a comic strip story. You may decide to encourage students to think of Joey and Jon as the heroes of the story. It would be a good idea to look at a selection of comics with students before they attempt this task. Look particularly at how the text beneath the pictures is usually used for narrative, whilst there may be speech bubbles for direct speech. In addition to this, there may be words such as 'zap' and 'pow' to add sound effects to the story.

Worksheet 20 sets the task of writing a newspaper article based on the dialogue on Worksheet 17. Before tackling this task, revise all that students know about the format of such articles. It would also be helpful to allow students time to look at a range of articles to make sure they have a full understanding of the task.

A dialogue

Worksheet 17

Name ____________________

- Read the dialogue below. It is a conversation between Joey and his friend Mike.

> *"Hi Mike, guess what happened to me last night."*
>
> *"You did your homework!"*
>
> *"No, much more exciting than that."*
>
> *"So what happened?"*
>
> *"Well, Mum let me go into town with my cousin Jon to see the new James Bond film."*
>
> *"Was it good?"*
>
> *"Dunno, I never saw it."*
>
> *"Why not?"*
>
> *"I'm trying to tell you if you'll just be quiet and let me."*
>
> *"O.K. get on with it then."*
>
> *"When Jon and I were walking through the town towards the cinema we saw the bloke that the police are looking for."*
>
> *"Were you scared?"*
>
> *"No, 'cos he hadn't seen us."*
>
> *"What did you do?"*
>
> *"Jon had his mobile with him and called the police. A few minutes later we saw blue lights and heard sirens – it was really exciting. The bloke ran off and some of the police chased him while two of them talked to us."*
>
> *"What did they want to talk to you about?"*
>
> *"They asked questions about what he was wearing, where he was heading and that sort of thing."*
>
> *"Did they get him?"*
>
> *"Yeah, but not until after they'd given us a lift home in the police car."*

Notes for teachers

By now, students are familiar with the layout and punctuation of written speech. Help them to read through the dialogue. You might like to explain to students that a dialogue is a conversation in written form. Explain that they will be asked to present the story in a different way. It is important that the students understand the story and the stages within it.

Prose

Worksheet 18

Name ______________________

- Use the dialogue from Worksheet 17 to complete the task below.

Write the story line from the conversation as a third person narrative aimed at an audience of children of about nine years old. You can add interesting details and a suitable illustration. Here are some ideas for ways to begin. You might have better ideas!

> "*One evening Joey's mum agreed to let him go with his older cousin to see a film, which was showing at the cinema in town.*"

> "*Day was turning to night as Joey and his cousin Jon started to walk into town.*"

> "*Joey was twelve years old and, after a busy day at school, was looking forward to an evening trip to the cinema with his thirteen year old cousin Jon.*"

____

____

____

____

____

____

____

____

____

____

____

____

____

____

Notes for teachers

Students must read the dialogue on Worksheet 17 before tackling this worksheet. Explain to the students the meaning of the words 'third person narrative'. They must understand that the 'third person' is the narrator describing the events. They are likely to need help in retelling the story.

A comic strip

Worksheet 19

Name ______________________

- Use the frame below to make the dialogue from Worksheet 17 into a comic strip story. There is space to write below each picture and you can also include speech bubbles and sound effect words. Before you start to write, plan how your complete story will fit into the six boxes provided.

Notes for teachers

Students must read the dialogue on Worksheet 17 before tackling this worksheet. As with Worksheet 18, the students must be able to break the story into its constituent parts. Encourage them to be creative with the text and with the illustrations.

A newspaper article

Name ______________________

Imagine you are a newspaper reporter. Write an article for the local newspaper based on the dialogue on Worksheet 17. Remember to write an eye-catching headline. Your first brief paragraph should give an overview of the story. You may wish to use imaginary quotes, from the police or one of the boys, in your report.

Notes for teachers

Support the students in considering the story again, this time seeking to present it in the style of a newspaper report. As an alternative to setting out the newspaper story on this sheet, you may wish to ask the students to work on the computer, laying out their page in two or three columns, and using appropriate fonts and text sizes to show headlines, and newspaper style print.

SECTION 5

Adding interest to writing

Notes for teachers

This short section helps students to consider ways to make their writing more interesting by adding adjectives and phrases to enrich sentences.

Before beginning this unit ensure that students clearly understand the term 'adjective'. It would also be valuable to revise the role of 'bracketing commas' and the way that they can improve a weak sentence.

Worksheet 21 can be completed by students working as a group or in pairs. It introduces the idea of adding adjectives and phrases to make sentences more exciting. Worksheet 22 follows the pattern of sentences established in the previous worksheet and asks pupils to choose their own words and phrases to produce some interesting sentences. It would be useful to work with pupils on using a thesaurus as this might help them to select interesting adjectives.

Whilst this work has been designed to give students as much freedom as possible, it might help to use the sentences below as examples of enhanced sentences.

1) The gnarled tree, covered in its summer green, stood in the corner of the field.
2) On top of the grassy hill, the family, sitting on a large red blanket, enjoyed their picnic.
3) The old carpet, faded from its original splendour, was green and beige.
4) The injured man, his face etched with pain, hobbled down the road.
5) My oldest friend, who comes to my house after school most days, likes to play computer games.
6) In the dark cave, sheltered from the freezing weather, the bear slept for the winter.

When Worksheet 22 has been completed and the results shared, you could ask students to suggest further ways of improving each of the sentences e.g. in sentence six they may suggest using an adjective to describe the bear. (The grizzly bear, the hibernating bear, etc.)

Exciting writing 1

Worksheet 21

Name ______________________

The two sentences below are about the same subject.
Read them both and discuss which you think is better and why.

It was a warm summer morning so Ike decided to go for a walk.

It was a glorious summer morning, the sky was a cornflower blue, so Ike decided to go for a walk.

Look at how the author changed the sentence to make it more exciting to read. The word 'warm' is a fairly ordinary word so the more powerful adjective 'glorious' was used to try to give a better idea of what the morning was like.

An extra phrase has been added to the sentence. Bracketing commas are added before and after this phrase as the sentence will still makes sense without it.

Look at the sentences below and choose the words and phrases that you think would make the sentences more interesting.

1) The **sleepy** dog lay, ______________, fast asleep in his basket.

Instead of sleepy:

tired	dozy
contented	exhausted

To add between the commas:

in front of a roaring fire	curled up peacefully	snoring loudly

____

____

2) The **flower** vase, ______________, was full of flowers.

Instead of flower:

shapely	ornate
tall	glass
porcelain	decorative

To add between the commas:

on the mantelpiece	her mother's favourite
the base covered with coloured glass stones	usually left empty

____

____

Notes for teachers

Read through the worksheet with the students ensuring that they understand the tasks. Remind them of the role of adjectives as words that describe. Revise the use of bracketing commas, encouraging the students to notice that the phrase between the commas adds information but is not crucial to the meaning of the sentence and could be omitted.

Exciting writing 2

Worksheet 22

Name ______________________

- Choose your own exciting words and phrases to make the following sentences more interesting. For each sentence you need to think of an adjective to fill the first gap and a phrase to fill the gap between the commas.
  Write your new sentences on the lines provided.

1) The ____ tree, _________, stood in the corner of the field.

2) On top of the _______hill, the family,______, enjoyed their picnic.

3) The ______ carpet,___________, was green and beige.

4) The _________ man, ______________, hobbled down the road.

5) My _______ friend,_____________, likes to play computer games.

6) In the ____ cave,________, the bear slept for the winter.

- Share your new sentences with the rest of the group.
  Can you suggest any other ways in which the sentences could be made even better?

Notes for teachers

This worksheet follows Worksheet 21 and contains sentences of a similar structure. The students are asked to think of words and phrases to fill the gaps. However, if they need help, you may like to dictate the complete sentences as shown in the *Notes for teachers* on page 30. This provides good practice in using phonic awareness to spell unknown words.

Planning a story

Notes for teachers

This section is about the process of planning a story in detail, particularly in relation to settings, characters and genres. It should be treated as an extended activity, taking place over several lessons but resulting in a well-written finished story.

Worksheets 23–26 pose the four questions: Where? When? Who? and What? (The question 'what?' is referring to the genre or style of the story). Students are encouraged to think of as many ideas as possible in response to these questions. Although the lists could be endless, you may need to provide some ideas, which could include the following:

- *Where?* School, classroom, woods, canal, river, beach, mountain, desert, motorway, street, village, town, city, factory, shop, shopping centre, etc.
- *When?* Yesterday, this morning, last night, at midnight, at dawn, at dusk, at noon, last week, last year, ten years ago, a hundred years ago, ten years from now, a hundred years from now, a thousand years from now, etc.
- *Who?* Myself, my best friend, my worst enemy, my sister, my brother, my mother, my father, my grandmother, my cousin, a teacher, a shopkeeper, a ghost, a dog, a police officer, a criminal, a van driver, etc.
- *What?* Humour, comedy, tragedy, murder, crime, romance, mystery, science fiction, adventure, fantasy, newspaper report, etc.

On Worksheet 27 the students are asked to use the information from the previous four worksheets to plan one story. They may need some help in choosing appropriately but the process of deciding *where, when, who* and *what* will help them to think of ideas for the plot itself.

Before committing themselves to the final story, the students should work through Worksheets 28–30 where they are given the opportunity to add greater detail to *where, when* and *who*.

It is important to keep the students well motivated with lots of encouragement for the effort that they put into developing ideas. They should use these ideas to attempt a first draft of a finished story and will need lots of help on remembering to add details to the settings, the timing and the characters.

At this stage, you could suggest that they draft the story on a computer so that they can print it out to edit it. Allow plenty of time for the editing and revising process. Encourage them to proofread their work before producing the final presentation of the text. If you prefer, instead of using a computer, the students could present the final work on plain paper using the line-guide on Writing template 1 (page 45).

Where?

Worksheet 23

Name ______________________

- All stories need a **setting** – the place where the events happen. Use this page as a planning sheet to develop ideas for places. Some ideas are provided for you – how many more can you think of?

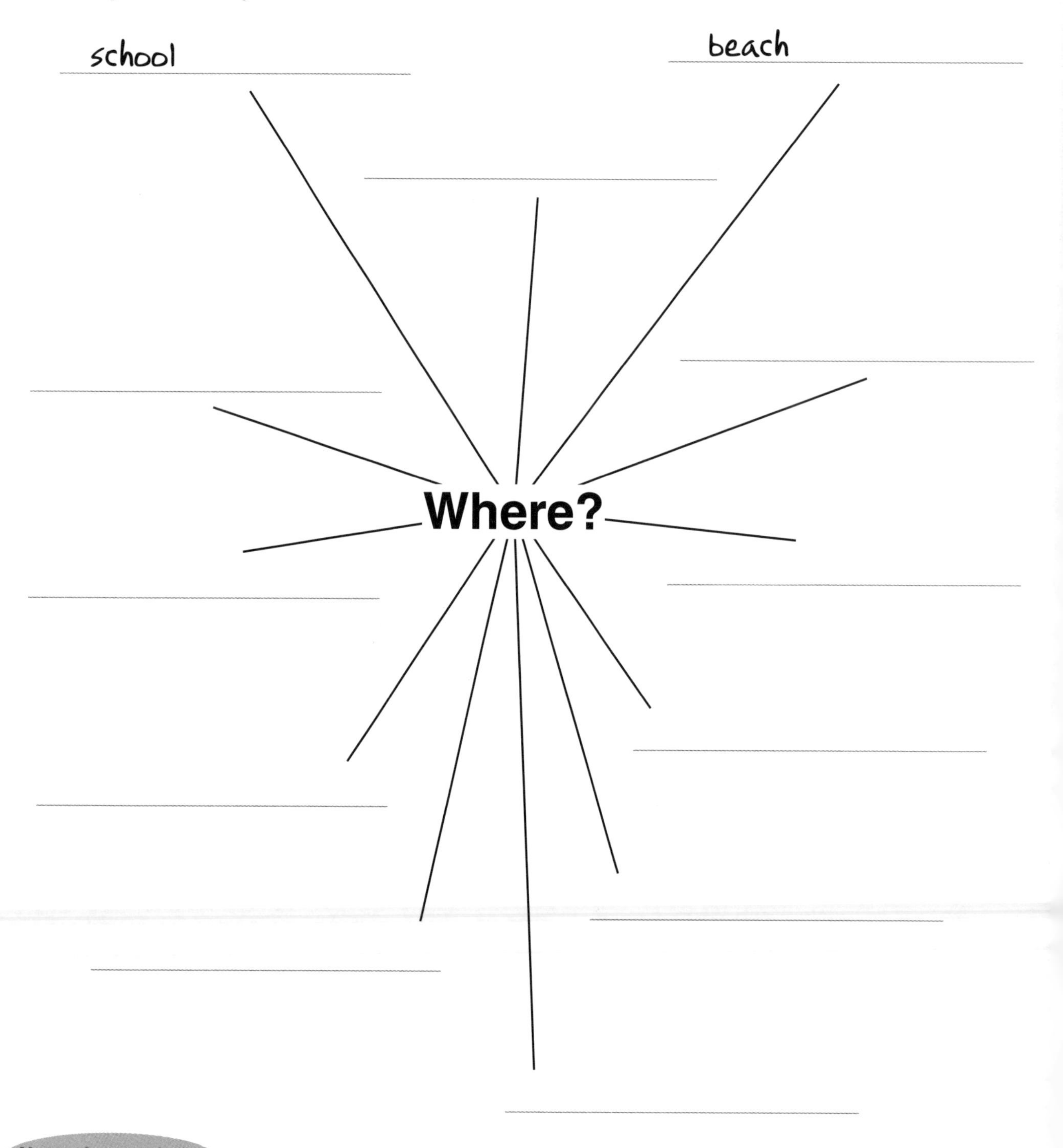

Notes for teachers

Help the students to think of as many ideas as possible for potential places to set a story. The list could be endless and you may wish to gather all the ideas together to create a class 'settings' bank – this could be used whenever you ask students to create a story.

When?

Worksheet 24

Name ____________________

All stories need a **time** when the events happen. Use this page as a planning sheet to develop ideas for times. Some ideas are provided for you – how many more can you think of?

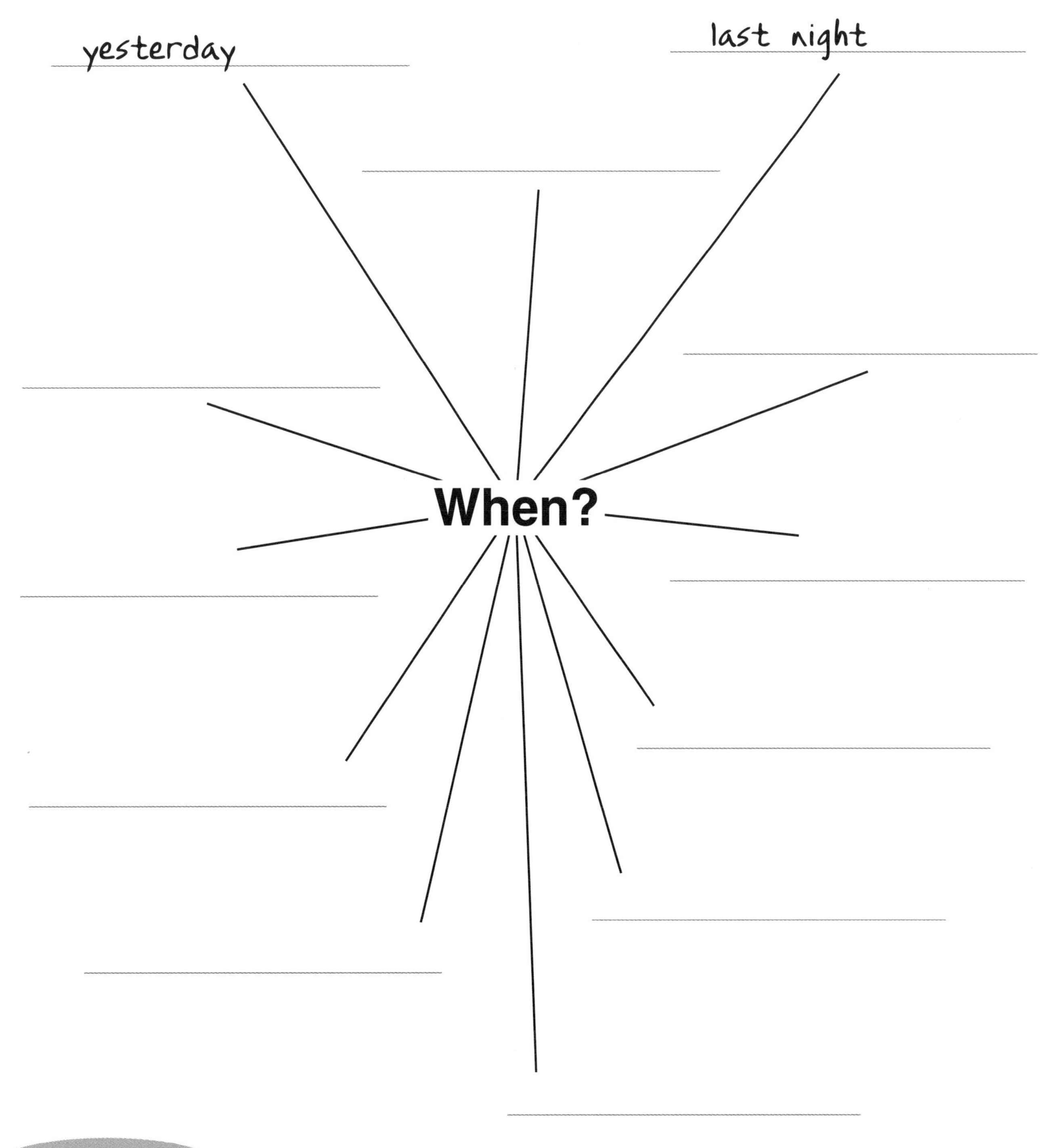

Notes for teachers

Help the students to think of as many 'times' as possible, such as the future, the past, even different time periods including Roman or Greek times for instance. This is more difficult than considering settings but, again, there are infinite possibilities.

Who?

Worksheet 25

Name ____________________

Every story needs **characters** – the people who are involved in the story. Use this page as a planning sheet to develop ideas for characters. Some ideas are provided for you – how many more can you think of?

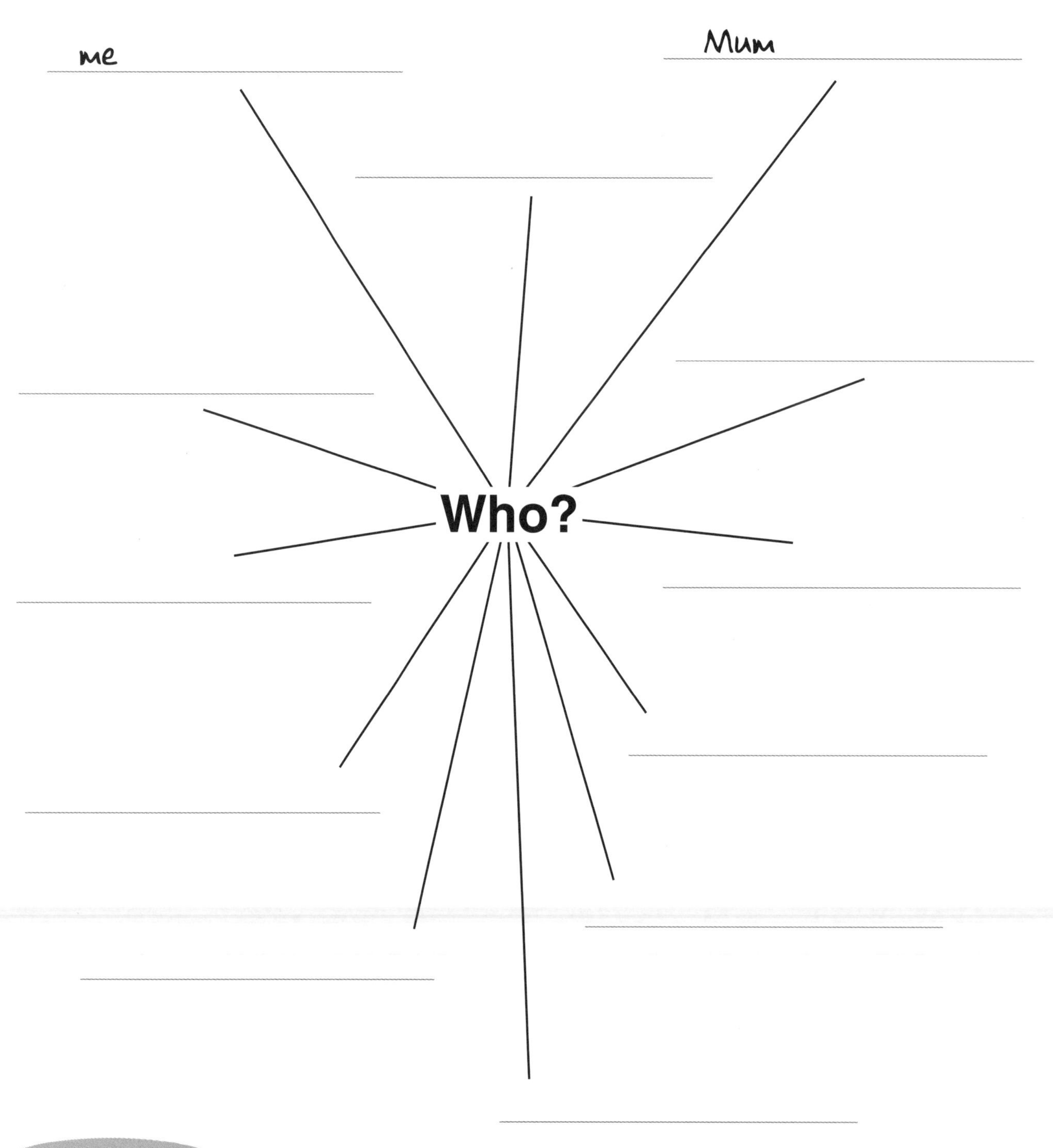

Notes for teachers

Much easier than considering settings or times, the possibilities for characters are endless. Characters can be identified by age, job, gender or as human/animal/alien.

Worksheet 26

What genre?

Name

You need to decide the *genre* of your story. *Genre* is a French word meaning kind or style. Use this page as a planning sheet to develop ideas for the genre of stories. Some ideas are provided for you – how many more can you think of?

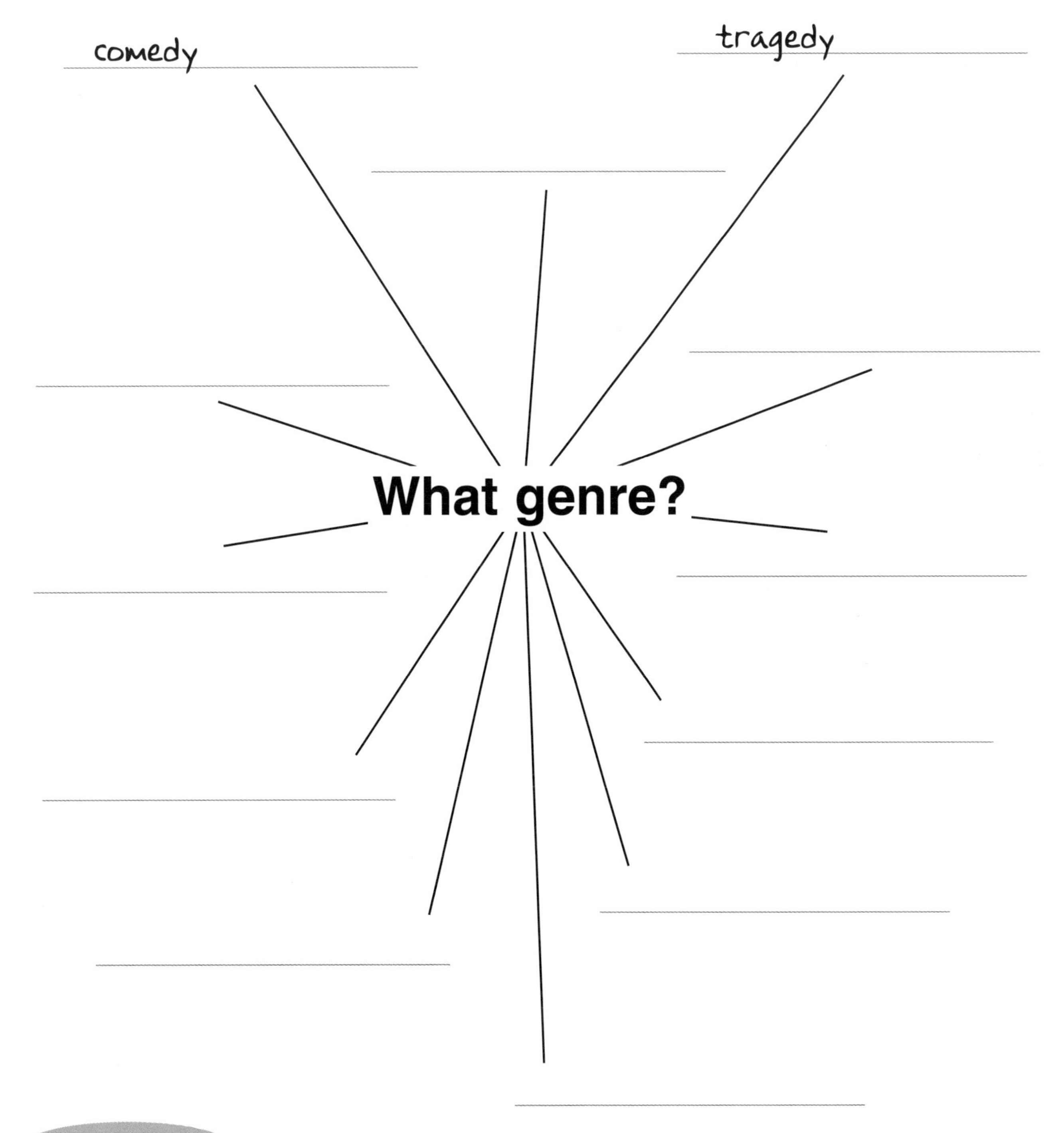

Notes for teachers

A more difficult task, students may need help in thinking of a variety of genres. You could help them by suggesting titles of books and asking them to identify the genre of each.

Planning the story

Worksheet 27

Name ______________________

You should have lots of ideas about **where** and **when** a story could take place, **who** could be involved and **what** genre could be used. On this sheet you need to choose from these ideas to create just one story.

Once you have decided on **where, when, who** and **what** you will need to develop ideas for the events that take place: how does your story start, how does it develop and how does it end?

Alternatively, you may want to decide the events before you specify **where, when, who** and **what**.

where

when

who

what

the start

the development

the ending

Notes for teachers

This planning sheet can be used to compile information from other sheets to help students to build a skeleton outline for their story. Once this sheet is completed, students should add flesh to the skeleton using Worksheets 28–30 before attempting the first draft of the complete story.

Worksheet 28

Planning the story 1: The setting

Name ______________________

- Now you know **where** your story is taking place you need to develop more details about it. On this page, write a detailed description for the setting of your story. Think about all aspects of where your story is set, then decide which of these are relevant e.g. the country, the town, the building, the room, etc.

  Now try to think of as many details as possible: What does the place look like? What can you see? What objects or features stand out? What is special about the features?

Notes for teachers

Students may need lots of help with this activity and may need to attempt it several times, adding more and more details on each occasion. Students may enjoy being challenged with questions that encourage them to think about the smallest of details in relation to features of the location.

Worksheet 29

Planning the story 2: The time

Name ______________________

Now you know **when** your story is taking place you need to develop more details about it. On this page, write a detailed description about the time when your story takes place. Think about all aspects of the time, then decide which of these are relevant e.g. the century, the year, the month, the time of day, etc.

Now try to think of as many details as possible: What is different about the time compared to now? What affect does the time have on the place? (e.g. the school at night will be very different from the school in the daytime.)

Notes for teachers

Students may need lots of help with this activity and may need to attempt it several times, adding more and more details on each occasion. Students may enjoy being challenged with questions that encourage them to think about the smallest of details in relation to features of the time.

Worksheet 30

Planning the story 3: The characters

Name ______________________________

Now you know **who** is in your story you need to develop more details about them. On this page, write a detailed description of the characters in your story. For each character, think about as many details as possible: How old is she/he? What does she/he wear? Is she/he moody, cheerful, depressed, excited, excitable and why is she/he like that? Does she/he have any distinctive features? Is she/he beautiful/ handsome?

Notes for teachers

Students may need lots of help with this activity and may need to attempt it several times, adding more and more details on each occasion. Students may enjoy being challenged with questions that encourage them to think about the smallest of details in relation to aspects of their story's characters.

Writing to argue, persuade or advise

Notes for teachers

This short section provides opportunities for students to write persuasively.

Worksheet 31 asks the students to present a piece of writing showing both sides of an argument. Some discussion will be needed to consider the word *argument* as they are likely to automatically think of a confrontational argument in which people are addressing each other, possibly aggressively and face to face.

Before completing the writing task you may decide to ask the students to debate the subject: *thirteen year-olds should be able to choose their own bedtimes*, appointing some students to argue *for* the motion and some to argue *against*. Can they think of good reasons for either viewpoint? The students are likely to argue strongly for one side or the other but encourage them to try to think of arguments for both sides – this will not be easy for them! When you think they are ready, ask them to complete the written task.

Worksheet 32 features a formal letter from a fictional parent to a fictional head teacher. Help the students to read the letter from a Mrs Fudge. Point out the structure of the letter: the positions of the addresses, the date and the 'signing off'. Discuss the importance of each of the four paragraphs: the first one stating the purpose of the letter, the next two showing Mrs Fudge's argument, the final one closing the letter but also repeating the request.

When you feel the students are ready, ask them to write a persuasive letter. This could be a letter asking for extra amenities and addressed to the head teacher of your school, a fictional head teacher or the local council. For a *formal* letter such as this, the students could write on plain paper using Writing template 3 (page 47).

Alternatively, the persuasive letter could be written to a friend asking them to come to an event because the writer is too nervous to go alone. This would be an *informal* letter for which the students could use Writing template 2 (page 46).

Worksheet 31

Writing to express an argument

Name ____________________

Thirteen year-olds should be able to choose their own bedtimes.

Do you agree with the statement above? If so, why?
Do you disagree with the statement above? If so, why?
Do you think that most thirteen year-olds would agree or disagree? Why?
Do you think that most parents would agree or disagree? Why?

- Can you write a balanced argument about the subject? A balanced argument shows both sides of the debate. At the end of the argument you could express your own personal view but you must make it clear that it's your own view.

Notes for teachers

Explain to the students that they are going to write an argument, pointing out that you are not asking them to write an imaginary 'argument' between two people but that you are asking them to write a mature, reflective piece of work that shows both sides of a debate. Encourage the students to discuss the motion thoroughly. Work through the questions with them, helping all students to express their viewpoint and offering particular praise to those who are able to express both sides of the argument.

Writing to persuade

Worksheet 32

Name ____________________

- Read this letter from a parent to the head teacher of her son's school.

23 Blagdon Road
Thornton
Staffordshire
TH14 7PR

Mrs E Johnson, MEd, Head teacher,
Thornton Community College
Westford Road
Thornton
TH2 9EE

22nd January 2008

Dear Mrs Johnson,

I am writing to ask whether it would be possible for Year 8 children to remain in the school buildings during the very cold weather.

My son, William Fudge, suffers terribly from chilblains behind his ears and these are made considerably worse by cold northerly winds such as those that we have been experiencing recently. He has tried to wear a hat to cover his ears but, unfortunately, some of the older children make fun of the bobble and ear-flaps and he is now too embarrassed to wear it.

Surely I am not the only parent to raise concerns regarding pupils spending so much time outside. I do not think that the teachers in your school would like to spend an hour outside in the cold at lunchtime, so why should the pupils?

Thank you for your attention to this matter. I look forward to hearing from you regarding whether the pupils will be allowed to stay indoors.

Yours sincerely,

Mrs Jane Fudge

- Now write your own persuasive letter on a subject that is important to you.

SECTION 8

Resource sheets

Notes for teachers

Writing templates (pages 46–48)
Each Writing template can be photocopied so the student can paperclip it behind a sheet of plain paper enabling her/him to write neatly without having to use lined paper. Talk about each part of the page before asking the student to fasten it with a paper clip.

- Writing template 1 is for story writing,
- Writing template 2 is for writing an informal letter
- Writing template 3 is for writing a formal letter.

Alphabet practice sheet (page 49)
Before using the Dictionary resource sheets you may like to encourage students to improve their alphabetical order speed. Help the students to draw lines to join the lower case letters to the matching upper case letters – don't allow them to complete the task in random order. This is quite a fun activity and can be used in a competitive way. Set the challenge of completing the task as quickly as possible. Students may like to work in pairs, with one person acting as the 'spotter' and one as the 'line-drawer', to try to improve their speed. This task can be repeated several times if you wish as it encourages the student to practise alphabetical order.

Word-finding practice sheet (page 50)
Ask the students to read the words out loud before they attempt this exercise. Once the exercise is completed ask the students to read the words that they found, ensuring that they understand what each word means. This activity can also be completed using a full-size dictionary instead of the 'mini' dictionary in this book – will the words found be different?

Dictionary resource sheets (pages 51–64)
The dictionary that can be created from the final fourteen sheets of this book is a very valuable resource. Once photocopied according to the instructions below, students should be able to fold it and carry it in blazer pockets or in their bags so that they can make use of it in other lessons.

To make the dictionary, photocopy the fourteen sheets to create master copies then photocopy the master copies, back to back, as follows:
Sheets: 1/2 Sheets: 3/4 Sheets: 5/6 Sheets: 7/8 Sheets: 9/10 Sheets: 11/12 Sheets: 13/14

The dictionary contains the more challenging of the high frequency and medium frequency words recommended for Key Stages 1 and 2, together with the words recommended for students in the early part of secondary school. We have deliberately included words that are not phonically regular. Explain to the students that they may not find every word they need in this dictionary but that they should always use their skills in syllabification and in phonics to attempt new words.

Each page of the dictionary has spaces for students to write their own spellings. This is an excellent way of encouraging the students to use their phonic knowledge to spell new words. When a student needs a word ask her/him to attempt the word by segmenting it into its phonemes. Give the student lots of praise where s/he is successful, even in part of a word, then write the word correctly on the line next to her/his attempt, stressing the phonemes and pointing out the graphemes that represent these.

Writing template 1

Writing template 2

This is where you write your own address. Make sure that you spell it correctly and that you include the postcode.

This is where you write the date.

Dear ...

Here you can write Yours sincerely, or Best wishes, or Love from,

This is where you write your name.

Writing template 3

This is where you write your own address. Make sure that you spell it correctly and that you include the postcode.

This is where you write the name and address of the person or the company you are writing to.

This is where you write the date.

Dear ... person's name, or Sir or Madam,

Here you can write: 'Yours sincerely', or 'Yours faithfully', if you have started with 'Dear Sir or Madam'.

This is where you write your name.

Alphabet practice sheet

Worksheet 33

Name ______________________

- How quickly can you join the pairs of letters?
- Draw a line to connect the **a** to the **A**, then another line to join the **b** to the **B**, etc.
- Time yourself.

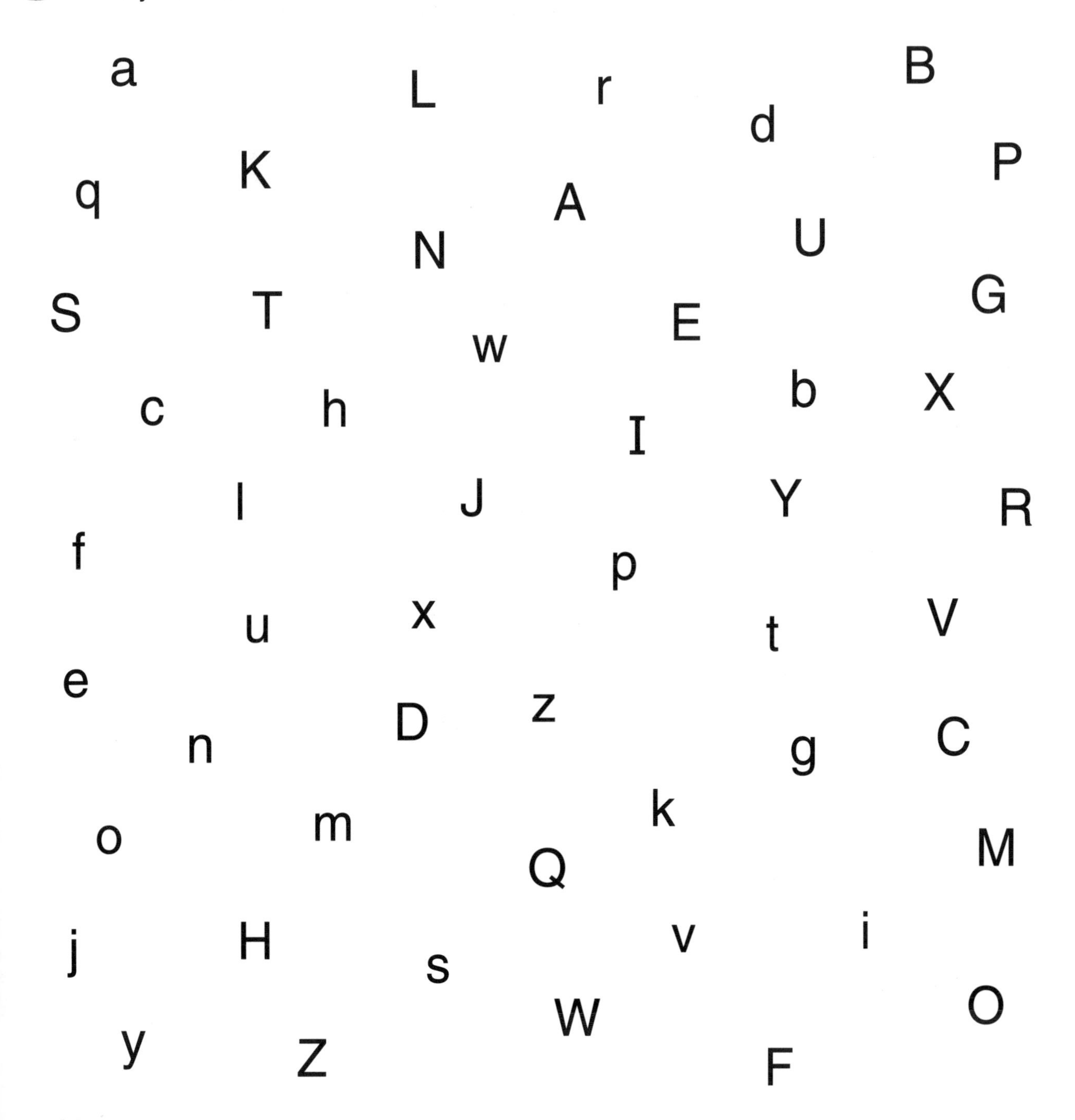

Notes for teachers

Support the students in drawing lines to join the lower case letters to the matching upper case letters – do not allow them to complete the task in random order. Set the challenge of completing the task as quickly as possible. This task can be repeated several times if you wish as it encourages the student to practise alphabetical order.

Word-finding practice sheet

Worksheet 34

Name ____________________

How quickly can you find the words?

Look through the dictionary, finding the word after each of the following words. Write them out neatly and with the correct spelling. Work as fast as you can: time yourself to see how quickly you can complete the whole page. Be careful as there may be time penalties for untidiness.

pen-friend ____________________

choose ____________________

dimension ____________________

together ____________________

under ____________________

mean ____________________

following ____________________

while ____________________

adventure ____________________

receive ____________________

height ____________________

caravan ____________________

opportunities ____________________

imagine ____________________

earth ____________________

Australia ____________________

country ____________________

strategy ____________________

night ____________________

beard ____________________

know ____________________

build ____________________

collection ____________________

DICTIONARY 1

Name ____________________

Days of the week	Numbers			
Monday	1	one	50	fifty
Tuesday	2	two	60	sixty
Wednesday	3	three	70	seventy
Thursday	4	four	80	eighty
Friday	5	five	90	ninety
Saturday	6	six	100	hundred
Sunday	7	seven	1000	thousand
	8	eight	1000000	million
Months	9	nine	1000000000	billion
January	10	ten		
February	11	eleven	first	
March	12	twelve	second	
April	13	thirteen	third	
May	14	fourteen	fourth	
June	15	fifteen	fifth	
July	16	sixteen	sixth	
August	17	seventeen	seventh	
September	18	eighteen	eighth	
October	19	nineteen	ninth	
November	20	twenty	tenth	
December	30	thirty		
	40	forty		

DICTIONARY 2

The alphabet

a b c d e

f g h i j k

l m n o p

q r s t u

v w x y z

A B C D E

F G H I J

K L M N O

P Q R S T

U V W X

Y Z

See how quickly you can write the alphabet.

a

z

A

Z

Name

Address

School name

Address

DICTIONARY 3

x X

y Y

year
yell
yelled
yelling
yellow
young
your
yourself

z Z

zero

a A

able
about
above
abroad
abroad
abstract
accident
accommodation
achieve
achievement
across
activities
activity
actually
address
adjective
adult
adventure
adverb
affect
afraid
after
afternoon
again
agriculture
aircraft
alarm
alcohol
alien
all right
allowed
almost
alone
along
also
although
always
amenity
analyse
analysis
animals
another
answer
answered
any
anyway
anywhere
apartment
apparatus
appearance
apple
approximately
area
argument
around
arrive
arrived
ask
asked
asking
aspect
assessment
assistant
athletics
atmosphere
attic
audible
audience
Australia
authority
autumn
available
average

DICTIONARY 4

b B

baby
balloon
banana
bark
barked
battery
beard
beautiful
because
before
began
beginning
believe
below
beneath
better
between
bicycle
birthday
black
blond
boast
boat
bonfire
bored
both
branch
brave
break
breakfast
brick
bright
broken
broom
brother
brought
brown
build
builder
building
bulb
bungalow
buried
business
busy

w W

Wales
walk
walked
walking
want
warily
watch
water
wear
wearing
weather
weekend
weight
weird
welcome
were
west
what
when
where
while
whisper
white
who
whole
why
window
winter
wire
wish
wishes
without
woke
woken
woman
women
work
world
worry
would
wrap
write
writing
wrong
wrote

v V

vegetables
vehicles
verb
vertical
very
village
vitamin

c C

called
came
camera
caravan
carbohydrate
carefully
castle
catch
cathedral
caught
celebration
centimetre
centre
cereals
chair
change
character
chase
cheerful
chew
children
chocolate
choose
chronological
cinema
circulation
citizen
city
classification
clean
clear
climate
climb
climbing
close
clothes
cloudy
coffee
collection
colonisation
colour
coloured
column
come
comes
coming
communication
company
compensation
complain
complaining
complaint
complete
component
computer
concentration
conclusion
confirmation
conjunction
connection
conscience
conscious
consequence
consider
constable
container
continue
continuous
control
conversation
corner
correct
costume
could
couldn't
countries
country
crazily
crazy
creation
cricket
cried
cries
cross
cruise
curly
currently
curtain
customer

DICTIONARY 6

d D

dangerous
dashboard
daughter
decide
decided
decimal
decision
definite
demand
describe
description
design
development
diagram
dialogue
diamond
diary
didn't
different
dimension
direct
disappear
disappoint
discussion
disease
distance
doctor
does
don't
door
down
downstairs
dressed
drove
during

u U

ugly
unconscious
under
unfortunately
uniform
United Kingdom
until
upstairs
urban
used

t T

tail
teach
teacher
teaches
technique
technology
teenage
telephone
television
temperature
template
texture
thank
theatre
their
there
these
thief
third
those
thought
thoughtful
thoughtfully
through
ticket
tiny
tired
together
tomorrow
tongue
tooth
tourism
towards
towel
train
transport
travel
travelling
tremble
tried
tries
tripped
trotting
trousers
trunk
trust
tumbled
type

e E

earlobe
early
earth
easily
east
eaten
economic
edge
electronic
eleventh
elsewhere
embarrass
emigration
employment
encourage
encouragement
energy
engagement
England
enjoy
enough
enquire
environment
evaluation
evaporation
evening
every
everybody
everything
evidence
example
excitedly
exciting
exclamation
exhibition
expensive
explanation
expression
eye
eyebrow
eyelashes

DICTIONARY 8

f F

fable
faithfully
family
father
fault
favourite
feature
February
fence
fibre
field
fierce
final
finally
fire
fireworks
first
flew
flower
follow
following
football
foreground
formal
forty
forward
found
frequency
friend
friendly
friends
frighteningly
front
fruit
fulfil
further
furthermore
future

s S

safety
said
sandwich
scare
scary
school
Scotland
screamed
second
secondary
section
sentence
separate
sequence
settlement
shadow
shampoo
sharp
shirt
shiver
shocked
shoes
shopkeeper
shopped
shopping
should
shoulder
shout
shouted
shouting
show
shower
shriek
sincerely
sir
sister
situation
sixth
sketch
skilful
skirt
sleepover
slice
slowly
small
smiled
smooth
snippet
soldier
some
something
sometimes
somewhere
sound
south
space
sparkling
speak
speaker
speaking
special
specification
spectrum
speech
spiky
spoken
spread
spring
started
stomach
stopped
stopping
straight
strange
stranger
strategy
strength
stuck
study
stupidly
style
subject
success
such
suddenly
summer
sure
surely
surprise
surprised
surprising
survey
suspended
swam
swerve
swerving
swimming
swoop

r R

racism
range
reaction
realise
really
receive
recipe
reference
reflection
refund
regional
regret
rehearsal
relief
religion
religious
remember
remove
replied
replies
reply
report
research
resources
rhombus
rhyme
right
rinse
roar
round
running
rural
running

g G

galloping
garage
garden
gentle
gently
ginger
girl
glass
gloomy
glue
goes
gone
good
government
grabbed
great
Great Britain
grey
ground
growing
guard
gymnastics

DICTIONARY 10

h H

habitat
hair
half
halfway
happen
happened
happily
happiness
happy
haunt
have
head
health
heard
hearing
hedge
height
helicopter
high
highlight
hobbies
hobby
holiday
homework
hopped
horizontal
horrible
horror
house
hover
huge
hundred
hunting
hurry
hygiene

q Q

quarter
question
questionnaire
queue
quick
quickly
quiet
quietly
quite

p P

paragraph
parallel
parents
parliament
participation
passage
passengers
pattern
peaceful
pen-friend
people
performance
permanent
person
personality
personification
persuade
persuasion
physical
picture
piece
pineapple

place
planes
playground
please
pocket
police
political
portrait
position
possession
possible
potato
potatoes
potential
preparation
present
presentation
pretty
prioritise
probably
process
production
promise

proportion
proposition
protect
protein
puzzle

i I

ideas
imaginary
imagine
immediately
immigrant
important
impossible
improve
improvement
improvise
incisors
include
including
inconvenience
independent
indirect
industrial
informal
information
ingredient
injury
inside

instructions
instrument
interesting
international
internet
interrupt
interview
introduce
introduction
invitation
invite
inviting
involvement
Ireland
irrelevant
isosceles
issue

j J

jacket
jealous
jigsaw
journey
juice
jumbled
jumped
junction

o O

o'clock
obvious
offer
officer
often
only
opened
opportunities
opportunity
orchestra
original
outdoor
outrageous
outside
over
overheard
overturned
oxygen

n N

narrative
narrator
national
natural
near
nearby
necessary
nervous
never
night
normally
north
Northern Ireland
notice
noun
nowadays
number
nurse
nutrition

k K

kiln
kitchen
knew
knife
knives
know
knowledge

DICTIONARY 14

l L

ladder
lady
landscape
later
laugh
launch
leaf
leaflet
lean
leap
leave
leaves
lemonade
letterbox
librarian
lifeboat
light
likely
listening
little
live
lived
living
load
lonely
lorries
loud
loudly
lounge
love
lovely

m M

machine
madam
magazine
mansion
many
marriage
match
material
matter
mean
meanwhile
middle
might
mineral
minutes
mirror
miscellaneous
mischief
mobile phone
modern
molars
money
moral
moreover
morning
mother
motorway
mouse
moustache
mouth
moved
murmur
muscle
musician
myself
mystery